Out of this World

AIRWAYS

Contents

1 Breathing Trouble 9

2 Prof's Plan 17

3 Locked In 25

4 The Green-Ox System 33

Nova Speak 40

by Sally Odgers

illustrated by Matt Lin

Reading Manga: What is it?

The Japanese word 'manga' has been used for nearly 200 years. It means whimsical pictures (man = whimsical, ga = pictures).

Today, manga is a label for Japanese-style graphic novels, comic books and animated movies (also called anime). What's the difference between a graphic novel and a comic book? The answer is in your hands. Graphic novels are usually quality productions, sometimes run to hundreds of pages, and often cover serious subjects. Many Japanese manga focus on topics like the environment, the law, science, history – you name it.

Manga don't all look exactly the same, but they have some things in common:

Big Eyes

Oversized Expressions

Fast Action

Reading Manga: How to Follow

Each page of a graphic novel is divided into boxes called panels. You follow the panels from left to right and top to bottom, like this:

Each panel is like a paragraph in a regular book. It shows you where the characters are, and what they are doing, saying and thinking.

Some panels include a little box at the top (or the bottom), giving you information about what's going on. These are called captions.

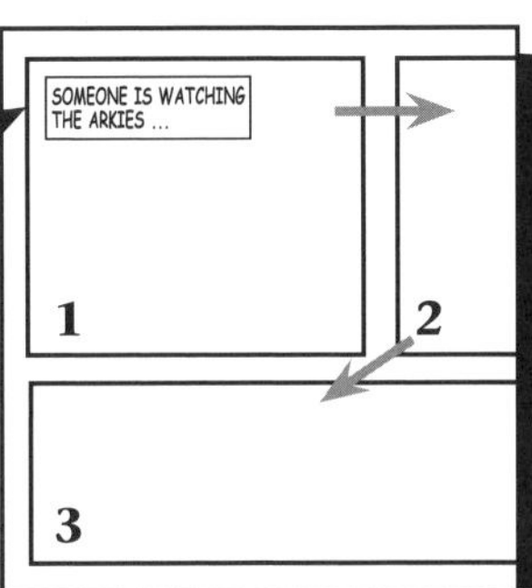

DID YOU KNOW?

Traditional Japanese manga look a little different. That's because in Japan, people read from right to left. Japanese manga is read like this:

It's easier than it looks!

Reading Manga:
Who's talking?

Speech balloons tell you who is speaking, what they're saying, and how.

Sometimes the lettering changes, to tell you which words are most important. These words might appear in **BOLD** or LARGE TYPE or in *ITALICS*.

Sometimes a punctuation point is enough to explain what's going on.

And how would you show an alien language? Maybe like this:

Reading Manga: What's that sound?

When you read speech bubbles, you hear manga characters' voices inside your head. There's a way to hear the background noises too – the rumble of thunder, the ringing of a telephone, the crack of a stick underfoot.

Manga artists represent sound effects (or SFX) by placing words over the panels, using lettering to suit each particular sound. It looks like this:

Scary sound

Mechanical sound

Quiet sound

DID YOU KNOW?

Japanese manga SFX are very precise. For example, *bicha bicha* means small splash, *bashan* is a medium splash, and *zaban* is a very big splash. There's even an SFX for total silence: *shiin*.
SFX are used to show emotions as well. The word *unzori* placed next to a character tells you they're feeling bored. If it was *moji moji* they'd be feeling shy, and *shobo shobo* indicates sadness.

Reading Manga:

What's that look on your face?

Manga characters have exaggerated expressions, to help you understand what they're feeling. The first feature everyone notices is the eyes, which may be wide open in:

Shock

Fear

Hope

Closed eyes can mean:

Laughter

Sadness

Noses and chins are more difficult to spot (some characters have no nose at all). This reflects the Japanese preference for delicate features. In manga, big noses and chins are kept for the bad guys.

Reading Manga:

What's that look on your face?

Just like manga characters' eyes, manga mouths are either huge or tiny. A big, wide-open mouth indicates:

Fear

Anger

Happiness

A character with a little mouth may be feeling:

Sad

Thoughtful

Shy

You can also tell a lot about manga characters from the crazy colour or style of their hair. For example, blue hair can mean the character is cool-headed, while orange hair equals determination (and sometimes a fiery temper). Wild, spiky hairstyles show the character is adventurous.

Three kinds of people live on Space Station Nova.

The Stationborn have been there for generations.

Zita

The Shipborn were born on giant spaceships that wander the Galaxy.

The Earthborn came to Nova from Earth.

There has always been rivalry between the three sets of Stationers. But one thing might bring them together: the game they call 3D.

TO PLAY 3D, YOU NEED TO BE VERY FIT ... THE MEMBERS OF GOLD TEAM JUNIOR TAKE FITNESS SERIOUSLY.

PROF, THE TEAM CAPTAIN, SETS THE PACE.
ON THE DOUBLE ... JEK, WHERE ARE YOU?
WAITING FOR NONNY.
WHY'S SHE SLOWED DOWN? WE'VE ONLY JUST STARTED.
IT'S SO STUFFY UP HERE, I CAN'T GET MY BREATH!
THERE'S NO ROOM TO RUN DOWN THERE.
NOVA'S GETTING SO CROWDED!
YES. THERE ARE TOO MANY SHIPBORN AND EARTHBORN COMING HERE.
IT'S MAYOR GAHDIAN'S FAULT. HE WANTS THE POPULATION TO GROW ...
BUT HE DOES SEEM TO KN MORE PEOP NEED MOR ROOM.

ON THE WALKWAY BELOW, LIKWITZ IS LISTENING.
THEY'RE ALWAYS BLAMING UNCLE FOR EVERYTHING.

IF DAD WAS AYOR, THINGS WOULD BE FINE.
HE WOULDN'T HAVE TIME TO COACH US IN 3D THEN.

HE DOESN'T HAVE MUCH TIME NOW. MAYOR GAHDIAN KEEPS MAKING HIM DO OTHER JOBS.

THERE THEY GO AGAIN.

MAYOR GAHDIAN HAS SUMMONED DOC TO HIS OFFICE.
HOW IS THE NEW JOB GOING, DOC? WELL, I TRUST?
NOT EXACTLY, MAYOR.
THE WHOLE VENTILATION SYSTEM NEEDS REPLACING. IT ISN'T UP TO THE JOB.
I AM SURE YOU CAN FIX IT. I HAVE EVERY FAITH IN YOU.
MAYOR GAHDIAN, THIS SYSTEM CAN'T COPE. IF YOU DON'T BELIEVE ME, ASK THE NEW MED-TECH!
WE DON'T HAVE THE BUDGET TO REPLACE IT THIS YEAR. YOU MUST DO THE BEST YOU CAN.

FINE! BUT I HOPE YOU REALISE WHAT COULD HAPPEN IF THE SYSTEM MALFUNCTIONS?
SOME PEOPLE MIGHT TAKE THAT AS A THREAT, DOC.

NO, MR MAYOR. IT'S A WARNING.
3D NOVA SHUTTLE DOCKING.
I MUST GO TO GREET THE SHUTTLE.

LD TEAM JUNIOR ALSO
EARS THE ANNOUNCEMENT.
LISTEN!
3D NOVA SHUTTLE DOCKING.

D BLUE
M MUST
E BACK!
DO YOU THINK THEY WON THEIR MATCH?

OF COURSE THEY WON! THEY ALWAYS DO.
THERE THEY GO ... SAYING BAD THINGS ABOUT UNCLE BUT THEY CAN'T WAIT TO SEE BLUE TEAM!

KWITZ VISITS
E MAYOR.
UNCLE? UNCLE? I THINK YOU SHOULD KNOW ...

VENT SYSTEM
ACCESS CODES
NORTH
A BLOCK
7456 : 9543 : 2469 : 3752
UNCLE? THIS LOOKS INTERESTING ... I COULD HEAR ALL SORTS OF THINGS FROM THERE.
O2
AIRLOCK CODES

HI, GUYS! HOW MUCH DID YOU WIN BY?
WE DIDN'T.
SORRY, KIDS. WE LOST.

BUT YOU ALWAYS WIN.
BLUE TEAM IS THE BEST!
EXCEPT FOR US ...

THIS TIME WE WEREN'T THE BEST.
WE'RE NOT AS FIT AS WE SHOUL BE. I CAN'T UNDERSTAND IT ...

C'MON, TEAM, BACK TO WORK.
I'M GOING HOME, PROF. MY HEAD IS ACHING.

NONNY'S
LWAYS GETTING HEADACHES NOW.
I DON'T FEEL VERY WELL MYSELF, DO YOU?
MAYBE WE SHOULD GO AND SEE A MED-TECH, IN CASE WE'VE ALL CAUGHT SOMETHING?
PROF AGREES.
GOOD IDEA, JEK. LET'S GO.
NONNY IS ON
HER WAY TO REST.
I WISH MY HEAD WOULD STOP THUMPING.
VENTILATION SYSTEM INSPECTION HATCH 6
CLONK-ONK
F, JEK AND ZITA VISIT
MED-TECH ROOM.
HELLO, ALI. WE WERE WONDERING IF—
LET ME GUESS. YOU FEEL TIRED AND BREATHLESS.
HOW DID YOU GUESS?
NO GUESSING NEEDED. I SEE FAR TOO MANY PEOPLE WITH THOSE SYMPTOMS.
NONNY OFTEN HAS HEADACHES.

I THOUGHT SO.
WHAT IS IT?
WHAT DID YOU DO? I FEEL BETTER!

I DIDN'T DO ANYTHING. IF YOU FEEL BETTER, IT'S BECAUSE OF THOSE.
THE PLANTS?

MED-TECH ALI EXPLAINS.
ON NOVA YOU HAVE AN ARTIFICIAL VENTILATION SYSTEM, BUT ON EARTH THERE IS NATURAL VENTILATION. DO YOU UNDERSTAND?
CO2
O2
NO.

HUMANS BREATHE OXYGEN, AND EXHALE CARBON DIOXIDE. PLANTS USE CARBON DIOXIDE AND PRODUCE OXYGEN.

SO YOUR PLANTS HERE ARE PUTTING EXTRA OXYGEN INTO THE AIR OF THIS OFFICE ...
AND THAT'S WHY WE FEEL BETTER!

ED-TECH ALI EXPLAINS THAT THE OLD VENTILATION
YSTEM CAN'T COPE WITH NOVA'S GROWING POPULATION.
... SO IT'S NO WONDER EVERYONE IS FEELING A BIT OFF COLOUR.
IS IT DANGEROUS?

NOT YET, BUT NO ONE IS GOING TO BE ON TOP FORM UNTIL SOMETHING IS DONE. I'VE TRIED TO TELL MAYOR GAHDIAN.
MED
SO THAT'S WHY BLUE TEAM LOST THE GAME!

THIS IS SERIOUS, GUYS. BLUE TEAM IS IN TROUBLE, AND SO ARE WE.
IT'S WORSE THAN THAT, PROF.

SPACE STATION NOVA IS IN TROUBLE.

LATER, IN PROF'S PRIVATE LAIR ...
THINGS CAN'T BE THAT BAD, JEK. OTHERWISE SOMEONE WOULD DO SOMETHING ABOUT IT.
SOMEONE IS. DO YOU REMEMBER I TOLD YOU MAYOR GAHDIAN KEEPS FINDING WORK FOR DAD?
YOU MEAN DOC IS WORKING ON THE VENTILATION SYSTEM?
THAT'S RIGHT.
MAYBE HE'LL FIX IT. DOC CAN DO MOST THINGS.
IT'S A PITY WE CAN'T ALL GROW ALI'S PLANTS.
THERE'S HARDLY ROOM FOR PEOPLE, SO WHERE WOULD YOU PUT THEM?
I KNOW! EVERYONE COULD HAVE SOME IN THEIR QUARTERS!
LATER, IN THE CABIN PROF SHARES WITH DOC ...
HAVE YOU FIXED THE VENTILATION SYSTEM YET?
NO. AND TODAY IT'S WORSE. I'VE BEEN HEARING WEIRD NOISES.

THE TEAM'S HAVING PROBLEMS WITH FITNESS. WE THINK PLANTS WOULD—
LOOK, PROF, THERE ARE MORE IMPORTANT THINGS IN LIFE THAN 3D!

THAT'S NOT WHAT YOU USED TO SAY.
SORRY, PROF ... I'M DOING THE BEST I CAN. THE WHOLE SYSTEM REALLY NEEDS REPLACING, BUT MAYOR GAHDIAN WON'T AGREE.

HE REALLY IS A JOKE. HOW HE EVER GOT ELECTED ...

IKWITZ, HIDING IN THE
NTILATION SYSTEM,
ERHEARS DOC'S WORDS.
DOC SHOULD BE THROWN OFF THE STATION FOR THAT.

DAD MUST BE REALLY WORRIED.
MAYBE YOU'LL BE ABLE TO FIX IT.
IT SHOULDN'T BE MAKING THOSE NOISES.

THERE MUST BE SOMETHING ... I KNOW!

IN HER CABIN, NONNY IS FEELING ILL.
GLONK-ONK
MY HEAD'S THUMPING AGAIN.

BEEP!
OH NO, PROF WANTS ME AT THE LAIR. I HOP HE'S NOT GOIN TO MAKE ME TRAIN.

WE FOUND OUT WHY YOU'RE FEELING BAD. NOVA IS RUNNING LOW ON OXYGEN, BECAUSE THE POPULATION HAS GROWN TOO FAST.
AND WE'RE GOING TO DO SOMETHING ABOUT IT.

WE ARE?
WE HAVE TWO PLANS. ONE IS LONG TERM, BUT THE OTHER WE CAN START RIGHT AWAY.

DAD THINKS THERE'S SOMETHING MAKING NOISES IN THE VENTILATION SYSTEM, SO WE ARE GOING TO INVESTIGATE.

HOW CAN WE DO SOMETHING DOC CAN'T?
EASILY. WHO IS BETTER AT PLAYING 3D – BLUE TEAM, OR US?

WELL – US. EVEN BLUE TEAM SAYS SO.
RIGHT! WHY?

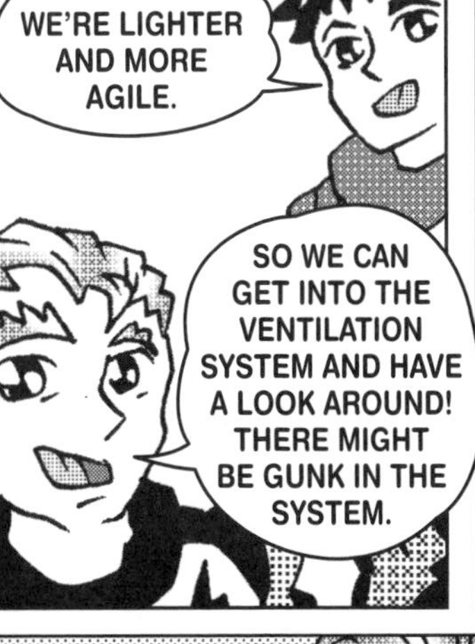
WE'RE LIGHTER AND MORE AGILE.
SO WE CAN GET INTO THE VENTILATION SYSTEM AND HAVE A LOOK AROUND! THERE MIGHT BE GUNK IN THE SYSTEM.

WHO'S GOING TO LET US DO THAT?
WE'RE NOT GOING TO ASK. NO ONE'S EVER SAID NOT TO.

ROF SHOWS THE TEAM A HOLO F THE VENTILATION SYSTEM.
I COPIED THIS FROM THE MAIN COMPUTER. YOU SEE WHERE THE SHAFTS BEND AND TWIST?
I BET THAT'S WHERE THE PROBLEMS ARE.

LATE THAT NIGHT ...
WHAT ABOUT THE ALARM? WON'T IT SOUND IF YOU BREAK A SEAL ON THE VENT SYSTEM?
I ... UM ... BORROWED DAD'S CODES.
THE MAIN INSPECTION HATCH IS IN THE OLDEST PART OF SPACE STATION NOVA.
VENTILATION SYSTEM INSPECTION HATCH 1
AIRFLOW
NORM
A SHOCK AWAITS THE TEAM WHEN THEY REACH THE HATCH.
DAD'S LEFT THIS HATCH UNSEALED!
I DON'T BELIEVE HE COULD BE SO CARELESS ... ANYONE COULD GET IN!
PROF LEADS THE WAY INTO THE HATCH.
BE CAREFUL, TEAM. WE MUSTN'T DO ANY DAMAGE.
THERE'S MORE ROOM IN HERE THAN I EXPECTED.
THIS IS THE MAIN LINE. THE BRANCHES ARE SMALLER.

LIKWITZ HAS FOUND A NEW GAME.
THIS IS GREAT!
CLO K-ONK
CLONK-ONK
IT LOOKS ALL RIGHT TO ME, APART FROM A BIT OF GUNK. MAYBE DAD WAS WRONG.
CLONK-ONK
CLONK-ONK
WHAT'S THAT? LISTEN ...
IT SOUNDS LIKE SOMEONE ELSE IS IN HERE ...
WHO? WHAT?

YOU CAN'T CATCH ME.

COME ON,
TEAM ...
QUICK!

IT WOULD
BE THEM. I'M
GETTING OUT
OF HERE!

FOOLED
THEM.

BETTER CLOSE
THE HATCH.
OTHERWISE
ANYONE MIGHT
GET IN.

chapter 3 : Locked In

I CAN'T HEAR ANYONE NOW. MAYBE WE WERE WRONG.

THE SHAFTS LOOK ALL RIGHT, DON'T THEY? THE AIR'S FLOWING NORMALLY. LET'S GO BACK.

WE'RE TRAPPED!

SERVES THEM ALL RIGHT.

HEY, LOOK AT THIS, A SPYGLASS! NOW WE KNOW WHO ELSE HAS BEEN IN HERE.
KLIKWITZ!

HUH? WHAT? OH-OH. BETTER GET OUT OF HERE!

CREEP, CREEP..
LET US OUT!
THE LITTLE CREEP MUST HAVE SHUT US IN! I CAN HEAR HIM SNEAKING AWAY.

MAYBE WE CAN STILL GET OUT ... PROF, IS THERE A GRILLE IN YOUR CABIN?
YES, THERE IS.
WHAT ARE WE WAITING FOR?
WHILE THE TEAM HEADS FOR DOC'S CABIN, KLIKWITZ HAS A PROBLEM.
THEY FOUND MY SPYGLASS! I BET THEY TRY TO GET ME INTO TROUBLE!
KLIKWITZ DECIDES ATTACK IS THE BEST FORM OF DEFENCE!
IT WOULD BE JUST LIKE THEM TO WRECK SOMETHING AND PUT THE BLAME ON ME.
I'LL DO A SPOT OF SABOTAGE THEN CALL UNCLE.

IT'S THIS WAY, AND WHEN WE GET TO A TURN-OFF WE NEED TO GO RIGHT.
I HOPE YOU KNOW WHERE YOU'RE GOING.

SOON ...
HERE WE ARE. NOW ...

KLIKWITZ HAS A PLAN ...
THIS VACUUM-BAG WASTE WILL DO THE JOB NICELY ...

DOC IS ASLEEP IN HIS CABIN ...
SCRITCH-SCRITCH-PSSST! DAD!

PSSST! DAD! DAD!
WHA – WHO IS IT? WHERE ARE YOU?

DAD, WE'RE SHUT INSIDE THE VENTILATION SYSTEM.
PROF? IS THAT YOU?

WHAT ARE YOU DOING? DO YOU KNOW THE HARM YOU COULD DO IN THERE?

MEANWHILE ...
THAT SHOULD DO THE JOB. HA-HA-CHOOOO!

KER-CHOOOOO!

YOU HAVE NO IDEA HOW MUCH TROUBLE YOU'RE IN – AND ME AS WELL!
PLEASE – JUST COME AND LET US OUT.

DOC LETS THE TEAM OUT. HE IS VERY ANGRY.
THANKS, DOC. WE THOUGHT WE WERE STUCK IN THERE FOR GOOD.
NONSENSE. IT WASN'T EVEN LOCKED. GO HOME. ALL OF YOU.
WE WERE TRYING TO FIND OUT WHAT WAS WRONG.
WE'RE NOT THE ONLY ONES WHO GOT IN THERE!
GO!
KER-CHOOOO!
WHAT'S THAT?
GO ON. I'LL TALK TO YOU IN THE MORNING.
KER-CHOOO!
DID YOU HEAR THAT?
I WISH MY HEAD WOULD STOP BANGING.

THE TEAM IS IN DISGRACE.

INSIDE THE VENTILATION TUNNEL ...
I'M LOCKED IN! THIS IS ALL THEIR FAULT!

SPACE STATION NOVA SLEEPS ...
BUT DOC IS A WORRIED MAN.
IT'S SO STUFFY IN HERE. MAYBE I COULD ADJUST THE AIR FLOW?
DOC IS NOT THE ONLY PERSON AWAKE.
I'M GONNA MAKE THEM PAY FOR THIS ...
DOC TRIES TO ADJUST THE AIR FLOW.
I'LL TURN IT UP TO MAXIMUM. MAYBE A GOOD FLUSH IS ALL THE SYSTEM NEEDS?
SSSSSHHHHH!!
SSSSHHHHHH!
KER-CHOOOOOO! KER-CHOOOOOOO! ARGHHH!

IF PROF BEHAVES LIKE THIS, HE'S NOT RESPONSIBLE ENOUGH TO BE TEAM CAPTAIN ...
MEANWHILE ...

ARGHHHHHH! I'M SUFFOCATING!

THIS IS ONLY THE BEGINNING.
12
ARE WE UNDER ATTACK?
WHAT'S HAPPENING?
13
KER-CHOOOOO
HELLLLLLP!

BACK IN DOC AND PROF'S CABIN ...
OH, NO! PROF! GET IN HERE!

UMMMM ...

LOOKS LIKE DUST FROM A CLEANER BAG. AND NO, WE DIDN'T PUT IT IN THERE.
I NEVER THOUGHT YOU DID! BUT—
KLIKWITZ!

GOTTA GO AND SHUT OFF THE AIR FLOW, NOW!

OH NO! I'M NEVER GOING TO GET THERE.

I'LL HAVE TO TELL THE MAYOR!
WAIT ... DAD, IT WAS KLIKWITZ IN THE VENT SYSTEM. HE LOCKED US IN. HE MUST HAVE GONE BACK IN WHILE WE WERE TALKING TO YOU!

THAT KID IS AS BAD AS HIS UNCLE! HOW AM I GOING TO GET TO THAT HATCH?

I'LL CALL THE TEAM! ONE OF US MIGHT BE ABLE TO MAKE IT.

PROF GOES INTO ACTION!
TEAM, WE NEED YOU!

GET TO THE VENT HATCH!

ANY WAY YOU CAN!

TURN OFF THE AIR FLOW!

THE TEAM MOVES OUT!

PROF ...
WAIT ...

IF HE CAN,
I CAN!
GERONIMOOOOO!

SPACE STATION NOVA IS IN A PANIC.
IN THE MAYOR'S CABIN ...
TIME FOR THE EMERGENCY OXYGEN SUPPLY.

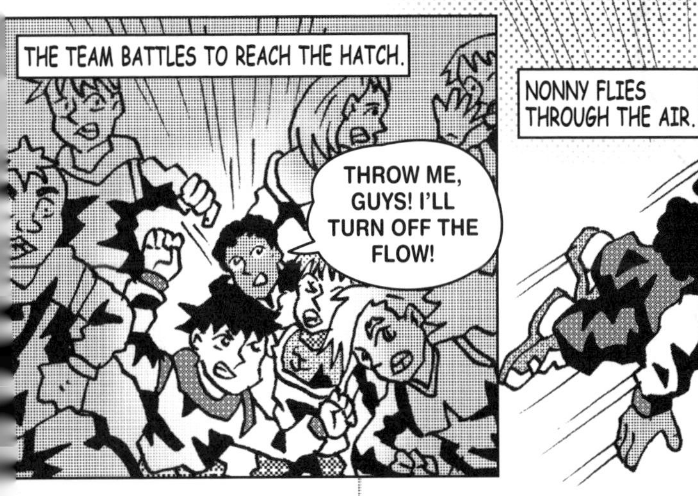
THE TEAM BATTLES TO REACH THE HATCH.
THROW ME, GUYS! I'LL TURN OFF THE FLOW!

NONNY FLIES THROUGH THE AIR.

MAYOR GAHDIAN! THIS IS AN EMERGENCY! GET PEOPLE BACK TO THEIR CABINS!
HE'S NOT ANSWERING. HE MAY BE ILL. WE NEED TO GET INSIDE.

DOC AND ALI CONFRONT THE MAYOR.
MAYOR, YOU MUST CONTROL THE SITUATION.
SO – YOU HAVE YOUR OWN EMERGENCY SUPPLY? GOOD. WE CAN FEED IT INTO THE SYSTEM.
GET OUT ... GET ...
O2

I'LL DO NO SUCH THING! THIS IS YOUR DOING, DOC!
NONSENSE. I'VE BEEN BEGGING YOU TO GET THIS SYSTEM REPLACED!
MAYOR GAHDIAN, DO YOU KNOW WHERE YOUR NEPHEW IS?
MED
O2

NONNY HAS TURNED OFF THE AIR FLOW.
GOT IT!
PLEASE EVERYONE, GO HOME!
ON

THE MAYOR ARRIVES.
EVERYONE, GO HOME! WE'RE PUTTING EXTRA OXYGEN INTO THE SYSTEM. GO NOW.
MAYOR G
O2
O2

KLIKWITZ! ARE YOU ALL RIGHT, BOY?
YOU MIGHT WANT TO ASK HIM WHAT HE'S BEEN DOING IN THERE WITH A DUST BAG!
UNCLE, YOU GOTTA GET RID OF THESE PEOPLE. THEY'RE BEING MEAN TO ME!

HUSH, BOY. DOC AND I HAVE IMPORTANT THINGS TO DISCUSS.
BUT THEY'VE BEEN SAYING—
MAYOR G

MUCH LATER ...
I NOW DECLARE THE BRAND-NEW VENTILATION SYSTEM OPEN!
STATION: 01 GOX GREEN-OX
WHEN THE GREEN-OX PLANT-BASED SYSTEM COMES ON LINE, WE WILL HAVE THE BEST STATION SYSTEM IN THE UNIVERSE!
. IS WELL AT SPACE STATION NOVA. TH THE NEW GREEN-OX SYSTEM COMING LINE, THE TEAM FEELS FIT AGAIN.
C'MON, GUYS – LET'S PLAY 3D!

JUST YOU WAIT. ONE DAY, I'M GONNA GET EVEN WITH ALL OF YOU.

Airways Nova Speak

3D A skilled ball game played on space stations.

Beeper A small communication device.

Earthborn People born on Earth.

Green-Ox system A ventilation system in which plants are grown to help provide oxygen.

Holo Holographic image. A picture that seems to float in the air.

Med-tech A technician who understands medicine and diagnostic equipment.

Shipborn People born on huge spaceships.

Stationborn People born on big space stations, like *Nova*.

Ventilation system A system that provides fresh air.